The Lie Detector

Dramatised from
Susan Gates' story
by David Calcutt

Illustrated by Ivan Bates

C000241001

Oxford University Press

Oxford University Press, Great Clarendon Street, Oxford OX2 6DP

Oxford New York
Athens Auckland Bangkok Bogota Buenos Aires Calcutta
Cape Town Chennai Dar es Salaam Delhi Florence Hong Kong
Istanbul Karachi Kuala Lumpur Madrid Melbourne Mexico City
Mumbai Nairobi Paris São Paulo Singapore Taipei Tokyo
Toronto Warsaw

and associated companies in
Berlin Ibadan

Oxford is a trade mark of Oxford University Press

© David Calcutt 1998

First published 1998

Adapted from the novel **The Lie Detector** by Susan Gates,
published by Oxford University Press in 1998.

ISBN 0 19 918788 6

All rights reserved. This publication may not be reproduced,
stored in a retrieval system, or transmitted, in any form or by any
means, without the prior permission in writing of Oxford
University Press. Within the UK, exceptions are allowed in respect
of any fair dealing for the purpose of research or private study, or
criticism or review, as permitted under the Copyright, Designs and
Patents Act, 1988 or in the case of reprographic reproduction in
accordance with the terms of licences issued by the Copyright
Licensing Agency. Enquiries concerning reproduction outside those
terms and in other countries should be sent to the Rights
Department, Oxford University Press, at the address above.

All applications for public performance of this adaptation should be
addressed in the first instance to the Permissions Controller,
Educational Division, Oxford University Press, Great Clarendon
Street, Oxford OX2 6DP.

Designed by Holbrook Design Oxford Limited

Printed in Great Britain

Cast list

Laura

Gemma

Harry

Father

Emily

Joanne

Laura is on stage right through the play.

Scene 1

*On stage there is a table and chair. **Laura** enters. She wears a school-bag over her shoulder and carries a box with two bulbs on top, one green and one red. On the front of the box, beneath the green bulb, is the word 'LIES'. Beneath the red bulb is the word 'TRUTH'. **Laura** puts the box down under the table, and speaks to the audience.*

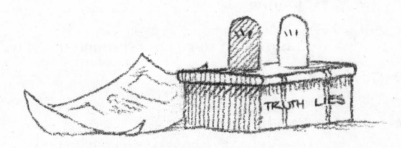

Laura   My name's Laura. My best friend's called Gemma, and there's just one thing wrong with her. She tells lies. And it's really stupid of her, because we all know they're not true. I'll give you an example. You see these trainers of mine? My mum bought them for me last week. Really expensive they were. I showed them to Gemma, and she thought they were great. Then yesterday, during library period at school, I'd just sat down and started to read, when Gemma came up to me, acting all excited.

Laura takes off her bag, hangs it over the back of the chair, and sits at the table. She takes a book out of her bag and opens it. Gemma enters, reading a book.

As soon as Gemma notices Laura, Gemma stops reading and goes up to her.

Gemma   Laura. My mum's got me some trainers.

Laura turns to Gemma.

Laura   Has she?

Gemma   Yes. Really expensive ones, like yours. Only mine have got purple flashes down the side.

Laura   Oh, yes? Where are these new trainers, then? Why aren't you wearing them?

Gemma   I'm not going to wear them for school! They'll
get spoiled. I'm keeping them for best.

> *Gemma turns away from Laura,*
> *and has her back to the audience.*
> *Laura closes her book, stands,*
> *and speaks to the audience.*

Laura I knew she hadn't got any new trainers. She was only saying it because I'd got some. It's the same whenever I have anything new. My mum buys me lots of clothes, and I always wear them to school, and a few days later, Gemma comes along, and she's had the same. She *says*.

Gemma turns to Laura.

Gemma My mum bought me some lovely silky black trousers yesterday. Just like the ones you're wearing.

Laura But you're not wearing yours.

Gemma	*(Hesitantly)* No...
Laura	Because you don't want to spoil them.
Gemma	Yes. That's right.
Laura	Oh, well. I'll have to come round and look at them some time, won't I?

Gemma speaks uncertainly.

Gemma   Yes, course you can, any time...

Laura turns and speaks to the audience.

Laura   She didn't have any new trousers. Just like she didn't have any new trainers. She doesn't have anything new. Everything she wears is hand-me-down stuff from her big sister. I don't mind that. So why does she pretend? And it's not only clothes. It's everything. Like – in my bedroom, I've got –

Gemma turns to Laura.

Gemma   So have I.

Laura   And I've got a computer of my own –

Gemma	And me.
Laura	And I've just had a video –
Gemma	I've got one too.
Laura	*(To the audience)* But she hasn't! She hasn't got any of those things. I've been to her house, and they've only got one TV and they haven't got a computer at all! So why does she bother lying? I hate it when people go about boasting and showing off like that. And I really caught her out with the video.

Laura turns to Gemma.

Laura	Gemma. You know you've just had a new video.
Gemma	Yes...
Laura	Why don't I bring round one of my films? I've got loads. We can watch my new Disney together in your bedroom.

Gemma looks confused.

Gemma	Er... that'd be great... only... we can't watch it today...

Laura	Why not?
Gemma	My video's gone to be mended...
Laura	I thought you said it was brand new.
Gemma	It is... only I spilt some orange juice on it... and smoke came out of it... and it's had to go back to the shop...
Laura	Oh, dear. That is a shame. Never mind. We'll have to watch it some other time.
Gemma	Yes... some other time...

Gemma goes.

Scene 2

Laura *puts her book back into her bag and speaks to the audience.*

Laura   I *do* like Gemma. Like I said, she's my best friend. But I'm getting fed up of all her lies. They're really pathetic, and she makes herself look silly telling them. So I've had a brilliant idea. I'm going to teach Gemma a lesson, for her own good. And I'm going to do it with this.

She brings the lie detector out from under the table.

Laura	It's a lie detector. My own invention. I made it from the electronics kit I had for my birthday. It's not a real lie detector, of course. But I'm going to tell Gemma it's real. And she'll believe me. I know she will. Because when I tried it out on my little brother yesterday, he did.

*Laura's brother **Harry** enters.*

Harry	What's that you've got there, Laura?
Laura	I'll tell you, if you let me ask you a question first.
Harry	All right, then.
Laura	Did you take the coloured pencils out of my bedroom?

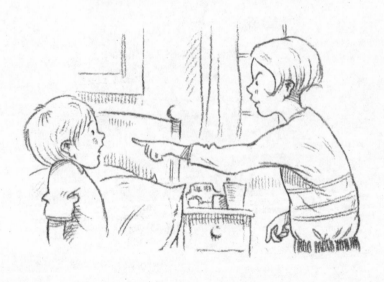

Harry	No, I didn't.
Laura	Are you sure?
Harry	Yes. Why are you blaming me?
Laura	Because I know you're telling a lie!

She holds up the lie detector. The green bulb is shining.

Laura	This is a lie detector. When you tell the truth the red light comes on. But when you tell a lie the green light comes on. And it's on now. So that means you told a lie.

The green light goes off.

Harry	A lie detector? You're joking.
Laura	I'm not, and I'll prove it. I'll ask you another question. Did your new school tie really get cut in half by accident?
Harry	Of course. It happened just like I told Mum. I got it trapped in the door.

The green light goes on.

Laura	No you didn't! Look! The green light's come on! You're lying!
Harry	I'm not –
Laura	*(In a spooky voice)* The lie detector always knows. It can read your mind.
Harry	I didn't do it – !
Laura	Tell the truth!
Harry	OK, OK. I'll tell the truth! I cut my tie with a pair of scissors. It was too long. It went down to my knees.

The green light goes off, and the red light goes on.

Laura	See? The red light's come on. That means you're telling the truth. Now. Did you take those pencils?
Harry	No, I didn't. Honest – !

The red light goes off, and the green light goes on.

Laura	Green light! Liar!

Harry   All right! I confess! I did take the pencils.

The green light goes off, and the red light goes on.

Laura   Red light! That's a good boy.

The red light goes off.

Harry   Let me have a go with that. I want to ask *you* some questions.

Laura   No! You might break it. You can ask me some questions, though. I'll hold the lie detector, and you can see if I tell the truth or not. Go on.

Harry   Did you eat the last chocolate yoghurt? The one
I was saving for myself?

Laura   No!

Harry   I bet you did. What does the lie detector say?

19

Laura holds up the lie detector.
The red light is on.

Laura   It says I'm telling the truth. Red. See?

          Harry is amazed and confused.

Harry   I don't understand. I was sure it was you.

Laura   You were wrong, then, weren't you? The lie
          detector says so.

          The red light goes off.

Harry   Where did you get it from, anyway?

Laura   Wouldn't you like to know? It's my secret.
          Want to ask me another question?

Harry   No. I don't like your lie detector. It's creepy
          having something read your mind like that.

Laura   Just because I found out you were lying!

          Harry turns to go. As he does,
          *their **father** enters.*

Father   What's the matter, Harry? You look upset.

Harry   Ask Laura, and her lie detector.

Harry goes.

Father	What's Harry talking about, Laura?
Laura	Oh, it's this, Dad. My lie detector.
Father	What?
Laura	I made it. Just for a bit of fun.
Father	How does it work?
Laura	There are wires going from these bulbs to a battery in the back. I've fitted two switches here. When I flick them, the bulbs light up. Red for truth, green for lies. See?

She turns the bulbs on and off.

Father	Why green?
Laura	When I was little, Gran used to say that if I told a lie my eyes would turn green.
Father	Oh, yes, I remember that.

Laura	It was silly, really. Because my eyes are green anyway. Do you think I'm clever, making this?
Father	I do. Very clever. But, did you tell Harry it was real?
Laura	Yes...
Father	Well, that was a lie wasn't it? I can tell, because your eyes have gone green.
Laura	It was only for a joke, Dad.
Father	A joke. I don't think Harry found it very funny.

Father goes. Laura speaks to the audience.

Laura	I think it's good, anyway. And it made Harry tell the truth, didn't it? I knew all along he'd taken those pencils and cut his tie, because I saw him. But he didn't know that I *did* eat that last chocolate yoghurt. That's the good thing about my lie detector. I can say what I like, and I'll always be telling the truth. And nobody knows but me! My brother's brainy, and he thought it was real, so it'll easily fool Gemma. And today, with my brilliant invention, I'm going to catch her out.

23

Scene 3

Gemma enters, with her friends Emily and Joanne. Laura speaks to the audience.

Laura   Here she comes, now. Just watch this.

Laura hides the lie detector and turns to Gemma.

Laura   Hello, Gemma.

24

Gemma   Hello, Laura. Hey, you know those roller-boots
               you had?

Laura   Yes?

Gemma   I've got a pair as well.

Laura   Have you?

Gemma   Yes, and they're just like yours, only instead of silver laces they've got gold ones.

Laura   Really?

Gemma   Yes.

Laura   Are you sure?

Gemma   Yes!

Laura takes out her lie detector.

Laura   Would you mind just saying it again, then?

Gemma looks at the lie detector.

Gemma   What's that?

Laura   This? Oh, nothing much. It's just a... lie detector!

Gemma   What?

Laura calls to Emily and Joanne.

Laura	Emily! Joanne! Come over here.

They come over to Gemma and Laura.

Emily	What do you want, Laura?
Laura	I want to show you my lie detector.
Joanne	Your what?
Laura	A machine for showing if you tell the truth or not. If you tell the truth, the red light comes on. But if you tell a lie, the green light comes on.
Emily	It's not real, is it?
Laura	Course it's real!
Joanne	Show us how it works, then.
Laura	We're just going to, aren't we, Gemma?
Gemma	Are we?
Laura	Just say that again about your new roller-boots. Go on.

Gemma speaks uncertainly.

Gemma   I've had some new roller-boots, with gold
laces –

The green light goes on.

Emily   Look! The green light's come on!

Laura   So it has. That must mean you're lying, Gemma.

Gemma   But I'm not!

The green light goes off.

Laura	All right, then. Let's try another question. Have you got your own TV in your bedroom like you said?
Gemma	Yes...

The green light goes on.

Joanne	*(Amazed)* The green light again!
Laura	It's no good lying, Gemma. The lie detector can read your mind. If you want the red light to come on, you've got to tell the truth –

The green light goes off.

Gemma suddenly shouts at
Laura.

Gemma   All right! I haven't got a TV in my bedroom! Or
a video! Or new trousers! Or a pair of roller-
boots! I haven't got any of those things! And I
know I shouldn't have said I had, but I couldn't
help it!

Gemma turns away from Laura,
very upset. *Emily* and *Joanne*
comfort her. The red bulb lights up
on the lie detector. *Laura* holds it
out towards Gemma.

Laura   Look, Gemma – the red light's on now... that means you told the truth...

Gemma is crying now. Emily and Joanne have their arms around her. Laura is surprised and shocked by this.

Laura   Don't you feel better now you've told the truth, Gemma – ?

Emily and Joanne snap at Laura.

Emily　　　What do you care how she feels!

Joanne　　I suppose you're happy you've upset her!

Laura　　　But it wasn't me! *I* didn't say she was telling lies.
　　　　　　　It was the lie detector. I didn't want to upset
　　　　　　　her. It wasn't anything to do with me –

> *Suddenly, the green light goes on.*
> **Laura** *is amazed.*

Emily　　　The green light!

Joanne	You've just told a lie, Laura!
Laura	No, I haven't! Look, Gemma. I'm sorry you're upset. We're still best friends, aren't we?

The green light goes off.

Gemma turns to Laura. She is trying not to cry.

Gemma	*(Bravely)* Yes, we are –

The green light goes on again.

Emily	Look! The green light's come on again!
Joanne	*(To Gemma)* That means what you just said wasn't true, Gemma.
Emily	And we know it wasn't true.

The green light goes off.

Joanne	Go on, Gemma. Tell her.

Gemma hesitates, then speaks to Laura.

Gemma	Right, then! I will tell the truth! The truth is I don't want you as a best friend any more, Laura!

Laura	What!
Gemma	You're a horrible best friend!
Laura	No, I'm not! I'm not a horrible friend!

The green light goes on.

Gemma	Yes, you are! The lie detector says you are!
Emily	Yes! She's right! You're always picking on Gemma.
Joanne	Always making fun of her.
Emily	You make her feel bad because she hasn't got new clothes and things!
Joanne	And you're always boasting and showing off!

Laura	No, I'm not! I'm not!

The green light flashes on and off.

Gemma	Look at your lie detector, Laura. It knows you're lying and we're telling the truth!
Laura	But it's not supposed to! It's not supposed to work like that! I wish I'd never made the stupid thing! I'm sorry I ever thought of it!

Suddenly, the green light goes off,
and the red light goes on.

Laura Look, Gemma. The red light's come on. That means I'm telling the truth! Listen to me, Gemma. I am sorry, really I am. I do like you. Can we still be friends? Please? I won't say nasty things about your clothes, and I won't show off any more. I mean it!

Gemma I don't believe you!

Gemma *walks off.* ***Laura*** *calls*
after her.

Laura	Don't walk off! Look! The red light's flashing! That means I'm telling the truth! Gemma!

She turns to Emily and Joanne.

Laura	Tell her, will you? Tell her I *am* sorry. I *do* want to be her friend. I mean it. The lie detector says so.
Emily	Perhaps you do mean it, Laura.
Joanne	But perhaps it's too late.

Joanne and Emily go.

The red light on the lie detector goes off.

Laura turns sadly, and walks to the table. She sits and puts the lie detector on the table.

Scene 4   *It is now that evening, at Laura's home. **Laura** examines the lie detector.*

Laura   I just don't understand it. This was supposed to do what I told it to. When that green light came on, I was pressing the red light switch! And I wasn't pressing a switch at all when the red light came on! Something must have gone wrong with it. Unless... unless it really did start to work... on its own... but it couldn't have done...

                 *Her **father** has entered and heard what she's saying.*

Father   Perhaps it was the wiring.

                 Laura looks up.

Laura   What?

Father   A couple of wires got crossed, perhaps.

                 He picks up the lie detector and starts to examine it.

Laura   Oh, yes. That was probably it.

Father	Anyway, there's somebody here to see you.
Laura	Oh? Who?

Gemma enters.

Gemma	Me.

Laura stands up. She's very pleased to see Gemma.

Laura	Gemma! I'm ever so glad you've come round.

Gemma	Are you? The lie detector's not saying anything.
Laura	It's broken.
Gemma	That's a shame. I'm sorry.
Laura	I'm not.
Gemma	Look, Laura. I just came to tell you... I will still be your friend.
Laura	Will you?
Gemma	Yes.
Laura	Oh, Gemma! I am glad! Really I am!
Gemma	I know you are. I can see that. Even without the lie detector!
Laura	The lie detector? Who needs it? Come on. Let's go up to my room –
Gemma	No. Let's go over to my house. Bring that new Disney film. Mum says we can watch it on our video. The one downstairs.
Laura	That'll be great! Come on!

Laura and Gemma start to go.
Father is still looking at the lie
detector.

Father   I could try to mend this for you if you like,
                    Laura.

                    Laura turns to him.

Laura	Er... don't bother, Dad. I think I'll throw it away. It's too dangerous. Unless you want it?
Father	Me? No, thanks.

> *He gives it to Laura, and goes. She turns to the audience.*

Laura	Or maybe one of you wants it? You can have it if you like. Only, don't blame me if it starts telling the truth.

*She puts it back on the table, and she and **Gemma** go.*

THE END

Treetops Playscripts
Titles in the series include:

Stage 10
The Masked Cleaning Ladies of Om
by John Coldwell;
adapted by David Calcutt
   single: 0 19 918780 0
   pack of 6: 0 19 918781 9

Stupid Trousers
by Susan Gates;
adapted by David Calcutt
   single: 0 19 918782 7
   pack of 6: 0 19 918783 5

Stage 11
Bertha's Secret Battle
by John Coldwell;
adapted by David Calcutt
   single: 0 19 918786 X
   pack of 6: 0 19 918787 8

Bertie Wiggins' Amazing Ears
by David Cox and Erica James;
adapted by David Calcutt
   single: 0 19 918784 3
   pack of 6: 0 19 918785 1

Stage 12
The Lie Detector
by Susan Gates;
adapted by David Calcutt
   single: 0 19 918788 6
   pack of 6: 0 19 918789 4

Blue Shoes
by Angela Bull;
adapted by David Calcutt
   single: 0 19 918790 8
   pack of 6: 0 19 918791 6

Stage 13
The Personality Potion
by Alan MacDonald;
adapted by David Calcutt
   single: 0 19 918792 4
   pack of 6: 0 19 918793 2

Spooky!
by Michaela Morgan;
adapted by David Calcutt
   single: 0 19 918794 0
   pack of 6: 0 19 918795 9

Stage 14
Petey
by Paul Shipton;
adapted by David Calcutt
   single: 0 19 918796 7
   pack of 6: 0 19 918797 5

Climbing in the Dark
adapted from his own novel
by Nick Warburton
   single: 0 19 918798 3
   pack of 6: 0 19 918799 1